I CAN FLY

BY RUTH KRAUSS

PICTURES BY MARY BLAIR

SIMON AND SCHUSTER · NEW YORK

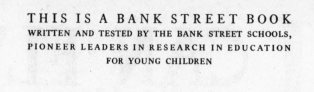

THIS IS A BANK STREET BOOK
WRITTEN AND TESTED BY THE BANK STREET SCHOOLS,
PIONEER LEADERS IN RESEARCH IN EDUCATION
FOR YOUNG CHILDREN

THIS IS A BRAND-NEW BOOK
WRITTEN AND ILLUSTRATED ESPECIALLY FOR
GOLDEN BOOKS

PUBLISHED BY SIMON AND SCHUSTER, INC.,
ROCKEFELLER CENTER, NEW YORK 20, NEW YORK
PUBLISHED SIMULTANEOUSLY IN CANADA BY
THE MUSSON BOOK COMPANY LTD., TORONTO

A bird can fly.
So can I.

A cow can moo.

I can too.

I can squirm

like a worm.

I can grab

like a crab.

Crunch crunch crunch

I'm a goat out to lunch.

Who's busy like a bee?

Me me me.

Who can walk like a bug?

Me! Ug ug.

I'm merrier

than a terrier.

Swish!

I'm a fish.

Pick pick pick

I'm a little chick.

Who can live in a hole?

Me! Like a mole.

Who can climb anywhere?

Me! Like a bear.

My house is

like a mouse's.

A clam

is what I am.

Pop pop pop

I'm a rabbit with a hop.

Bump bump bump

I'm a camel with a hump.

Haw haw haw

I'm a donkey in the straw.

Pitter pitter pat

I can walk like a cat.

Howl howl howl

I'm an old screech owl.

Gubble gubble gubble
I'm a mubble in a pubble.
I can play
I'm anything that's anything.
That's MY way.

I CAN FLY

Gayly   Words by Hilda Marx   Music by Alec Wilder

mf

I can fly like a bird, I can swim like a fish, I can grab like a crab, I can be what I wish.

Just by pre-tend-ing all through the day, I can be an-y-thing I want to play— That's my way.